This diary belongs to:

....

....

....

First published 2017 by Macmillan Children's Books
an imprint of Pan Macmillan
20 New Wharf Road, London N1 9RR
Associated companies throughout the world
www.panmacmillan.com

ISBN: 978-1-5098-4173-8

1 3 5 7 9 8 6 4 2

A CIP catalogue record for this book is available from the British Library.

Printed in China

With Tove Jansson's original illustrations

The MOOMIN
Colouring Diary

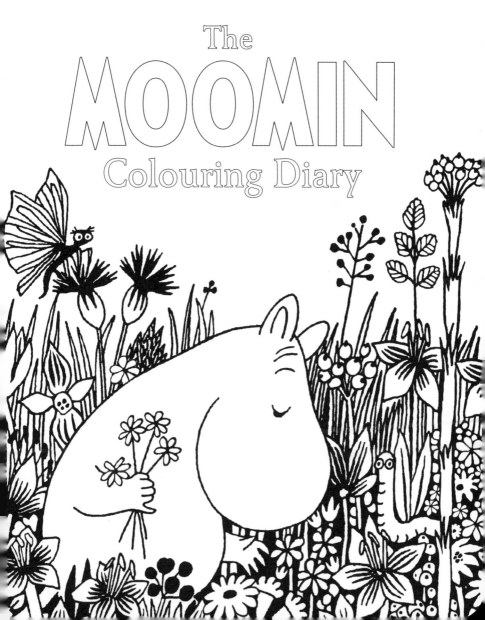

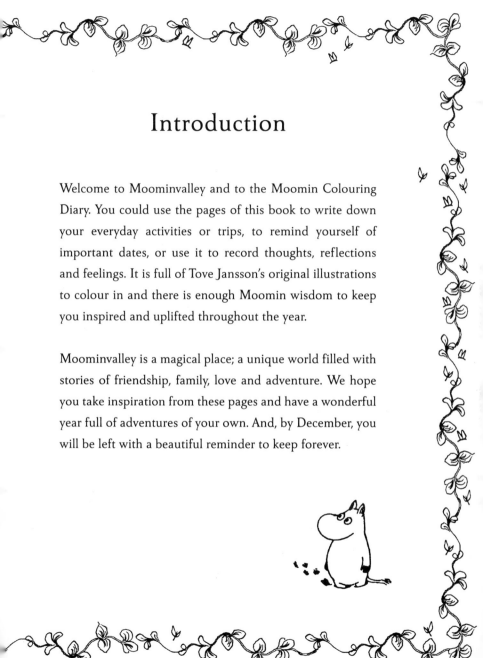

Introduction

Welcome to Moominvalley and to the Moomin Colouring Diary. You could use the pages of this book to write down your everyday activities or trips, to remind yourself of important dates, or use it to record thoughts, reflections and feelings. It is full of Tove Jansson's original illustrations to colour in and there is enough Moomin wisdom to keep you inspired and uplifted throughout the year.

Moominvalley is a magical place; a unique world filled with stories of friendship, family, love and adventure. We hope you take inspiration from these pages and have a wonderful year full of adventures of your own. And, by December, you will be left with a beautiful reminder to keep forever.

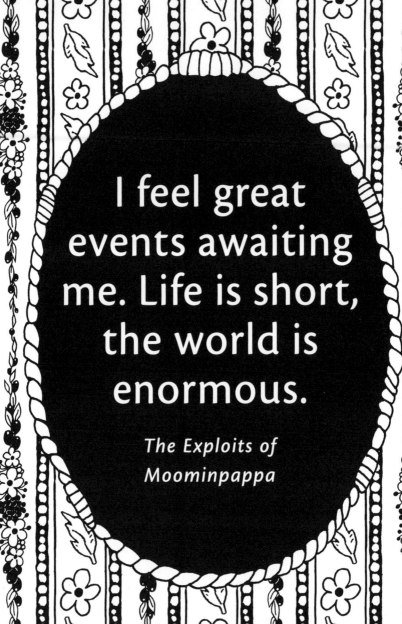

I feel great events awaiting me. Life is short, the world is enormous.

The Exploits of Moominpappa

JANUARY

1

2

3

4

5

6

7

JANUARY

8

9

10

11

12

13

14

JANUARY

15

16

17

18

19

20

21

JANUARY

22

23

24

25

26

27

28

JANUARY

29

30

31

NOTES

'Isn't life exciting,' Moomintroll thought. 'Everything can change all of a sudden, and for no reason at all!'

Moominpappa at Sea

FEBRUARY

1

2

3

4

5

6

7

FEBRUARY

8

9

10

11

12

13

14

FEBRUARY

15

16

17

18

19

20

21

FEBRUARY

22

23

24

25

26

27

28

FEBRUARY

29

NOTES

'The world is full of great and wonderful things for those who are ready for them.'

Moominpappa
Moominpappa at Sea

MARCH

1

2

3

4

5

6

7

MARCH

8

9

10

11

12

13

14

'All nice things are good for you.'

The Exploits of Moominpappa

MARCH

15

16

17

18

19

20

21

MARCH

22

23

24

25

26

27

28

MARCH

29

30

31

NOTES

Everywhere befuddled little creatures just woken from their long winter sleep poked about rediscovering old haunts and busied themselves airing clothes, brushing out their moustaches and getting their houses ready for the spring.

Finn Family Moomintroll

SPRINGTIME TO-DO LIST

My heart
has always
longed for new
places and new
acquaintances.

*The Exploits
of Moominpappa*

APRIL

1

2

3

4

5

6

7

APRIL

8

9

10

11

12

13

14

'I'll think about that tomorrow. I've more
important things on my mind now.'

Moominpappa at Sea

APRIL

15

16

17

18

19

20

21

APRIL

22

23

24

25

26

27

28

APRIL

Of course you have to feel free.

Tales from Moominvalley

29

30

NOTES

'One has to discover everything for oneself.'

Too-Ticky
Moominland
Midwinter

MAY

1

2

3

4

5

6

7

MAY

8

9

10

11

12

13

14

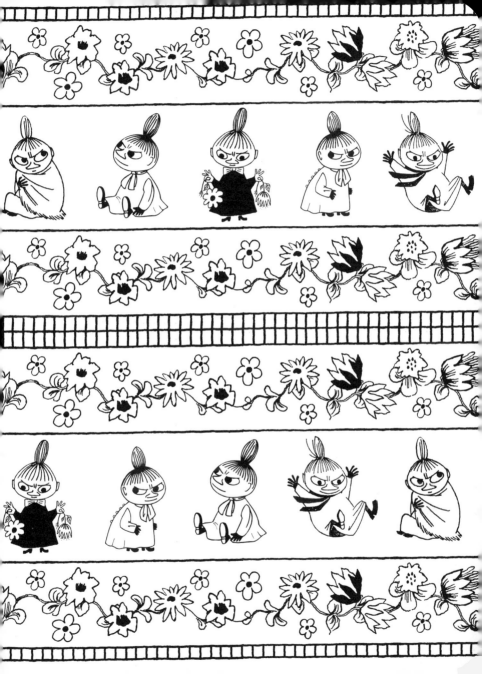

'And besides one gets so tired of
everlastingly sitting in the same place.'

Finn Family Moomintroll

15

16

17

18

19

20

21

MAY

22

23

24

25

26

27

28

'How nice to be on your own
for a bit and do what you like.'

Moominland Midwinter

MAY

29

30

31

NOTES

'Oh, how wonderful!
Oh how beautiful!'

Snorkmaiden
*Moominsummer
Madness*

JUNE

1

2

3

4

5

6

7

JUNE

8

9

10

11

12

13

14

JUNE

15

16

17

18

19

20

21

JUNE

22

23

24

25

26

27

28

JUNE

29

30

NOTES

'There are some things one can be absolutely sure of: sea currents, the seasons, the rising of the sun, for example.'

Moominpappa
Moominpappa at Sea

JULY

1

2

3

4

5

6

7

'It would be awful if the earth exploded.
It's so beautiful.'

Comet in Moominland

JULY

8

9

10

11

12

13

14

JULY

'Only bad people fare badly.'
Moominsummer Madness

15

16

17

18

19

20

21

JULY

22

23

24

25

26

27

28

The air was sweet with the smell of flowers.

Finn Family Moomintroll

JULY

29

30

31

'I would save your life eight times a day if only I could.'

Snorkmaiden
Comet in Moominland

AUGUST

1

2

3

4

5

6

7

AUGUST

8

9

10

11

12

13

14

For if you're not afraid how
can you be really brave?

The Exploits of Moominpappa

AUGUST

15

16

17

18

19

20

21

AUGUST

22

23

24

25

26

27

28

AUGUST

29

30

31

NOTES

'One must be alone sometimes.'

Moomintroll

Finn Family Moomintroll

'You must go on a long
journey before you
can really find out
how wonderful home is.'

Snufkin
Comet in Moominland

PLAN AN AUTUMN ADVENTURE

_____

_____

_____

_____

_____

_____

_____

_____

_____

_____

_____

_____

_____

_____

_____

_____

There are those that stay at home and those that go away, and it has always been so.

Moominvalley in November

SEPTEMBER

1

2

3

4

5

6

7

SEPTEMBER

8

9

10

11

12

13

14

'What a pity mothers can't go off
when they want to and sleep out of
doors. Mothers, particularly, could
do with it sometimes.'

Moominmamma
Moominpappa at Sea

SEPTEMBER

15

16

17

18

19

20

21

SEPTEMBER

22

23

24

25

26

27

28

SEPTEMBER

29

30

NOTES

'Let's steer straight ahead and just roll and sleep and never arrive anywhere!'

The Joxter
The Exploits of Moominpappa

OCTOBER

1

2

3

4

5

6

7

OCTOBER

8

9

10

11

12

13

14

15

16

17

18

19

20

21

OCTOBER

22

23

24

25

26

27

28

OCTOBER

29

30

31

NOTES

There's nothing as
lovely as being comfortable
and nothing is so simple.

Moominvalley in November

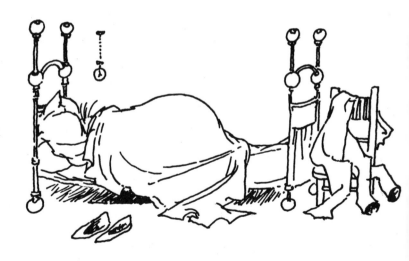

COSY WINTER PLANS

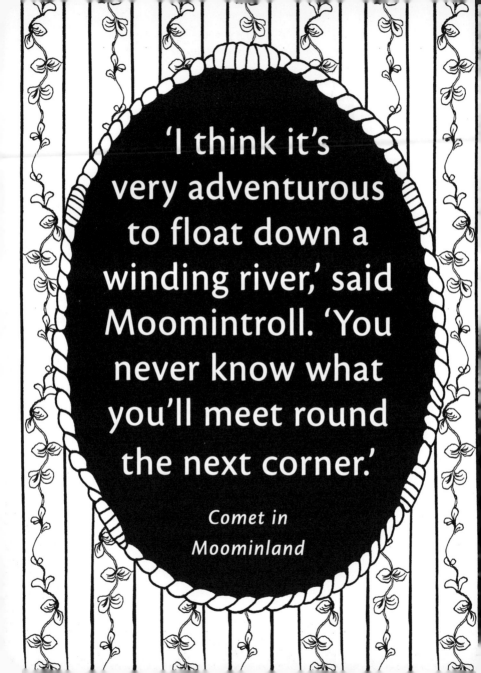

'I think it's very adventurous to float down a winding river,' said Moomintroll. 'You never know what you'll meet round the next corner.'

Comet in Moominland

NOVEMBER

1

2

3

4

5

6

7

NOVEMBER

8

9

10

11

12

13

14

NOVEMBER

'One learns to take the
rough with the smooth.'

Moominpappa at Sea

15

16

17

18

19

20

21

NOVEMBER

22

23

24

25

26

27

28

NOVEMBER

29

30

NOTES

'Mamma, wake up,' Moomintroll said anxiously. 'Something's on. They call it Christmas.'

Tales from Moominvalley

DECEMBER

1

2

3

4

5

6

7

DECEMBER

8

9

10

11

12

13

14

DECEMBER

15

16

17

18

19

20

21

DECEMBER

22

23

24

25

26

27

28

DECEMBER

_____

29

_____

30

31

_____

NOTES

_____

_____

_____

_____

_____

_____

_____

_____

_____

A new door to the
Unbelievable, to the Possible,
a new day that can always
bring you anything if you
have no objection to it.

The Exploits of Moominpappa

NEW YEAR'S RESOLUTIONS

NOTES

NOTES

NOTES

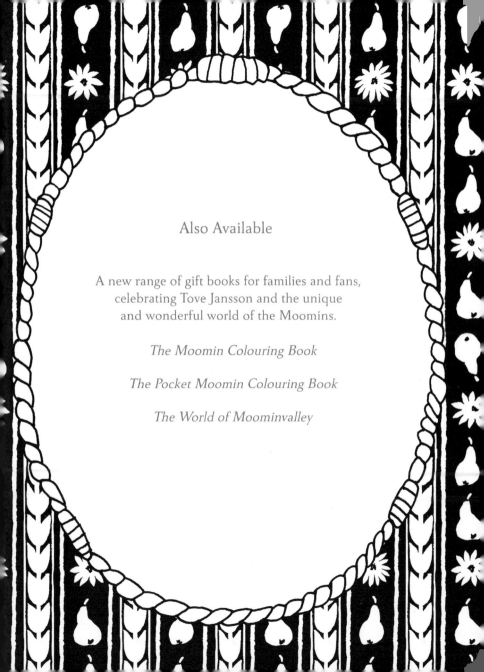

Also Available

A new range of gift books for families and fans, celebrating Tove Jansson and the unique and wonderful world of the Moomins.

The Moomin Colouring Book

The Pocket Moomin Colouring Book

The World of Moominvalley